THE KINGFISHER
NURSERY TREASURE CHEST

MARGARET CARTER

ILLUSTRATED BY
MOIRA AND COLIN MACLEAN

Kingfisher Books

For Jonathan and Helen

Open the treasure chest
Lift up the lid.
Such pleasures are waiting
So do as I bid.

Pictures to please you,
Puzzles to tease you,
So lift the lid wide
And see what's inside . . .

Kingfisher Books, Grisewood & Dempsey Ltd,
Elsley House, 24–30 Great Titchfield Street,
London W1P 7AD

First published in 1991 by Kingfisher Books

Text copyright © Margaret Carter 1991
Illustrations © Colin and Moira Maclean 1991
All rights reserved

BRITISH LIBRARY CATALOGUING IN PUBLICATION DATA
    Carter, Margaret
    The Kingfisher nursery treasure chest.
    1. Activities
    I. Title   II. Maclean, Colin   III. Maclean, Moira
    790.1922

ISBN 0 86272 805 3

Cover design by Pinpoint Design Company
Edited by Vanessa Clarke and Karen Gray
Photoset by Rowland Phototypesetting Limited,
Bury St Edmunds, Suffolk
Colour separations by Scantrans PTE Limited, Singapore
Printed in Spain

About this book

I've written this book for children and for grown-ups to share with their children, but every page has a hidden purpose – teaching and learning through enjoyment.

Numbers, letters, shapes, colours – all these are explored through games, stories and ideas for creative activities. And because a child responds most readily and remembers most easily through rhythm I've written many of the pages in verse.

I have carefully planned the pages so that you'll naturally find yourself developing and extending the ideas they contain – tailoring them to suit the child you are sharing with. For example, some children will love to join in and imitate the way animals move or the sounds they make; others will enjoy telling the stories in the pictures in their own words. Through asking questions and relating the pictures to their own world, you can help your child make his or her own discoveries about time and the seasons and many other themes.

This is a book that is meant to be dipped into for ideas that suit the moment. Better still, let your child choose the page where you begin. He or she will want to return to their favourite pages again and again. Most of all have fun together. After all, learning begins with listening and watching and talking – and it's a two-way business.

Margaret Carter

Contents

I See With My Eyes

I see
with my eyes

I smell
with my nose

I touch
with my hands

Voices and sounds

Babies hear before they are born –
their mother's heartbeat and,
distantly, the sound of voices or
music. Newborn babies hear high
pitched sounds more easily than lower
notes.

When a monkey hangs
From a banana tree
What do you think
That monkey can see?

He sees the earth
On top of the sky
And trees on their heads –
He wonders why.

He sees animals
Walking upside down
The world is so strange
It makes him frown.

But when he swings
Upright into his tree
It's all back the way
It's intended to be!

I Hear With My Ears

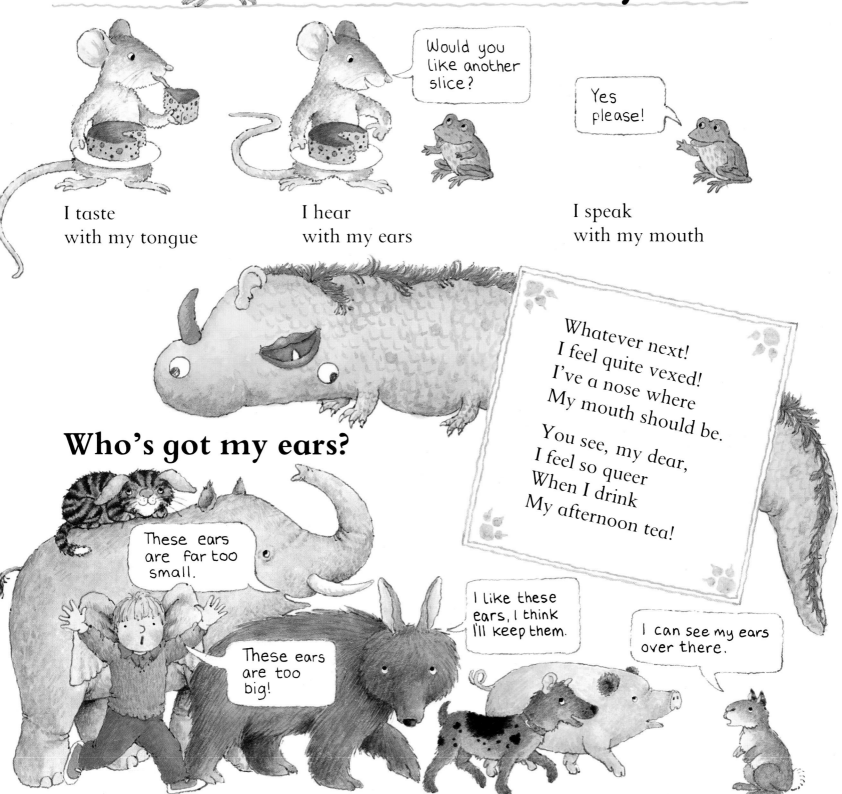

I taste
with my tongue

I hear
with my ears

Would you like another slice?

Yes please!

I speak
with my mouth

Who's got my ears?

Whatever next!
I feel quite vexed!
I've a nose where
My mouth should be.

You see, my dear,
I feel so queer
When I drink
My afternoon tea!

These ears are far too small.

These ears are too big!

I like these ears, I think I'll keep them.

I can see my ears over there.

'Squeak' Says the Mouse

squeak

hiss

moo

miaouw

baa

quack

too-wit
too-woo

Squeak, hiss,
Miaouw, moo,
Baa, quack,
Too-wit, too-woo.
Woof, maah,
Buzz, caw,
Neigh, oink,
Growl, ROAR!

buzz

caw

nee-igh

growl

woof

maah

oink

roar

Ollie's Orchestra

This is Ollie. Ollie is an octopus.
Ollie has a tambourine.
Ting, ting, ting-a-ling goes the

Ollie has a flute.
Toot, toot, toot goes the
ting, ting, ting-a-ling goes the

Ollie has some castanets.
Click, clack, clickety-clack go the
toot, toot, toot goes the
ting, ting, ting-a-ling goes the

Ollie has a violin.
Twang, twang, twang goes the
click-clack, clickety-clack go the
toot, toot, toot goes the
ting, ting, ting-a-ling goes the

Ollie has a drum.
Boom, boom, boom goes the
twang, twang, twang goes the
click-clack, clickety-clack go the
toot, toot, toot goes the
ting, ting, ting-a-ling goes the

"But now," says Ollie,
"I'm quite worn out!
I've tooted and clacked,
And twanged and whacked,
I've shaken and banged
And made such a din
That my head's in a spin!
Now I need a rest – don't you?"

The Animals' Dance

Make your own musical instruments and dance to songs you know.

Musical instruments to make

◀ Make a twizzer. Snip small triangles from the edge of a cardboard circle. Thread string through two central holes; tie the ends. Hold one loop in each hand and spin the twizzer to hear it hum – just like a bumble bee!

▲ Make a slither box with some dry sand in a long flat box. Seal the lid with tape and decorate. Move the box gently from side to side and hear it hiss!

◀ Old biscuit tins or large coffee tins make noisy drums and different kinds of beaters make different sounds.

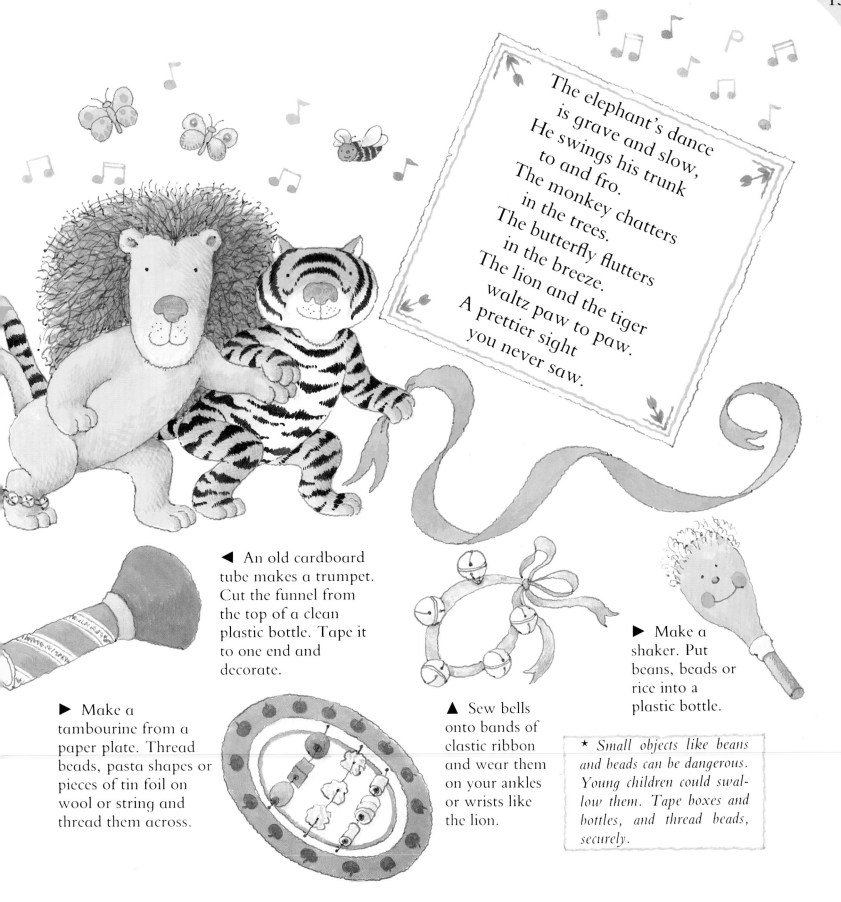

The elephant's dance
is grave and slow,
He swings his trunk
to and fro.
The monkey chatters
in the trees.
The butterfly flutters
in the breeze.
The lion and the tiger
waltz paw to paw.
A prettier sight
you never saw.

◄ An old cardboard tube makes a trumpet. Cut the funnel from the top of a clean plastic bottle. Tape it to one end and decorate.

► Make a tambourine from a paper plate. Thread beads, pasta shapes or pieces of tin foil on wool or string and thread them across.

▲ Sew bells onto bands of elastic ribbon and wear them on your ankles or wrists like the lion.

► Make a shaker. Put beans, beads or rice into a plastic bottle.

★ *Small objects like beans and beads can be dangerous. Young children could swallow them. Tape boxes and bottles, and thread beads, securely.*

Legs Are For . . .

crawling

toddling

walking

running

hopping

A centipede was happy quite, until a toad in fun, said, "Pray, which leg goes after which?"

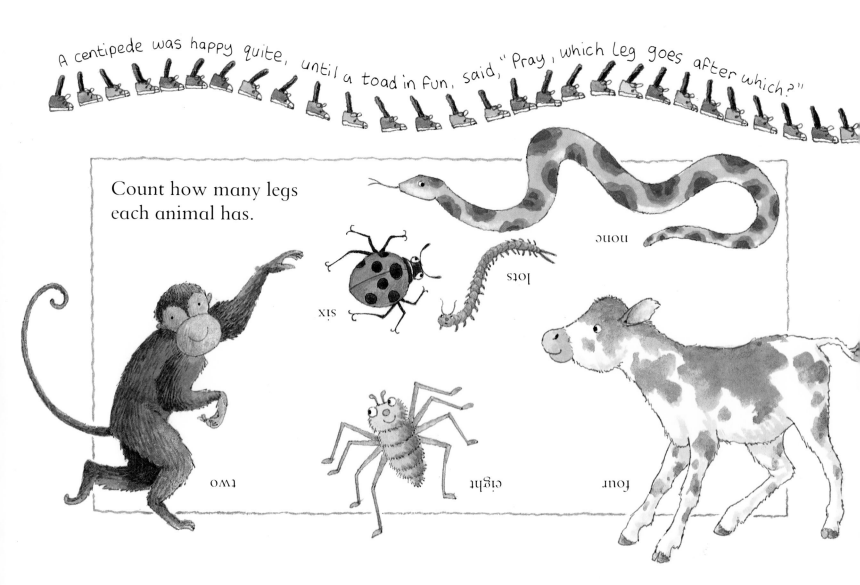

Count how many legs each animal has.

six

lots

two

eight

four

jumping   skipping   three-leg racing   wheelbarrow racing

This worked his mind to such a pitch, he lay distracted in a ditch, considering how to run!

All the legs are muddled up!
Can you sort them out?

Prowl Like A Tiger

Can you prowl like a tiger,

wriggle like a worm,

scamper like a mouse,

flutter like
a butterfly,

creep like
a caterpillar,

or fly like
a bird?

Can you scuttle
like a crab,

bound like
a kangaroo,

hop like a frog,

or leap like a deer?

stamp like a hen,

Children you are
very little,
And your bones are
very brittle.
If you would grow
great and stately,
You must learn to
walk sedately!
R. L. Stevenson

All Jump Up

Bellringer

Pull down the rope
Make the bells ring.
They'll play you a tune
As they merrily swing.

I whirl and I twirl
And I sing as I spin,
The faster I spin,
The louder I sing!
The slower I turn,
The quieter the sound,
And there's no sound at all
If I lie still on the ground.

Painter

Reach up high
Paint to the top.
Waggle your brush
Slip, slap, slop!

Drummer

Bang, bang, bang your drum
Beat it with a will.
Bang, bang, what a noise
I can hear it still!

Dancing

Try the Animals' Dance on page
12 or Mirror Dancing, where you
copy someone else's movements.

Dance like the mirror
Do as I do
Now change places
And I'll copy you.

Indoor gym

You don't need special equipment to make an obstacle course. Build one with ordinary objects at home. Make sure all the equipment is securely fixed and not too far from the ground.

Step on the stepping stones,
Mind you don't fall!
(They're really only cushions
Not stepping stones at all.)
Put them in a pattern,
Lay them on the ground,
Then you'll reach the other side
Safe and sound.

▲ A tunnel of cardboard boxes.

▶ Pillows or cushions for stepping stones or mats to roll on.

▶ A sandpapered, varnished plank of wood with the corners rounded down is a slide. Support it in the middle to make a seesaw.

▲ A rope or the plank raised on bricks makes a good balance.

Wouldn't It Be Funny . . .

Wouldn't it be funny
If cows made honey
And all the bees in the world
Said moo?

Wouldn't it be weird
If a worm grew a beard
And a tiger hopped
Like a kangaroo?

Wouldn't it be fun
If an ant weighed a tonne
And a hippo
Croaked like a frog?

Then supposing a cat
Could fly like a bat
Or a parrot could bark
Like a dog.
Well I wouldn't like that
Would you?

Peter Piper picked a peck
   of pickled pepper
A peck of pickled pepper
   Peter Piper picked;
If Peter Piper picked a peck
   of pickled pepper,
Where's the peck of pickled pepper
   Peter Piper picked?

How much wood
   would a woodchuck chuck
If a woodchuck
   could chuck wood?

I saw Esau
Sitting on a seesaw.

Fuzzy Wuzzy was a bear,
A bear was Fuzzy Wuzzy.
When Fuzzy Wuzzy lost his hair,
He wasn't Fuzzy, was he?

Paint, Paint, Paint

Plain or coloured scrap paper is fine for painting. Buy powder or poster paint and see page 92 for recipes to thicken paint.

Mirror painting

Fold a piece of paper in half and paint blobs of different colours down the crease. Refold, press firmly and open out – you've made a butterfly!

Make a non-spill paint pot

Cut a plastic washing-up liquid bottle in half and remove the nozzle top. Push the top half inside the bottom half, with the narrow end pointing downwards. A brush can be pushed through the narrow opening.

Bubble painting

Mix washing-up liquid with thin paint in a bowl and blow gently through a straw until bubbles form. Press a sheet of paper lightly over the bubbles. Or put a blob of paint onto the paper and blow through the straw so that the paint makes patterns.

★ *This isn't suitable for very young children, who might suck instead of blow.*

Invisible pictures

Draw a picture with a white wax candle. Paint over it with thin paint and the picture will appear.

Stencils

Cut a shape out of thin card and paint inside it. Make a doily by folding a piece of paper into four. Snip out shapes and open out then paint through the holes.

Spray painting

Dip a piece of wool or string into paint, then lay it on the paper. Fold the paper over and slide out the string. Do it again to make more complicated patterns.

String pictures

Only do this if you have plenty of space! Dip a toothbrush into paint and spray it onto paper by running a finger over the top. Try putting objects onto the paper first and spraying around them to make a pattern.

Body Painting

Non-toxic face paints aren't expensive and wash off easily.

Try a little on the child's hand first to check he or she isn't allergic to it.

Thick paint is best for body and face prints and, again, check that your child is not allergic to it.

The pictures opposite show the kind of effects you can create using hand, foot and nose prints.

Wellie prints

Fill a tray with paint. Place a road of paper along the ground and walk through the paint and along the paper. The ridges on wellies make interesting patterns, or try it with bare feet. A squirt of washing-up liquid added to the paint makes it easier to wash off afterwards. This is an activity best done on a washable floor!

bird

worm

fish

crocodile

Hop on one foot,
Now make a jump.
Walk on tiptoe
Or stamp – clump,
clump, clump
See what patterns
Your wellies can make
But stay on the paper
For goodness sake!

The Colour Race

For this game you will first need to make a colour spinner or colour brick – see below. You will also need to find or make a counter for each player.

Spin the spinner or throw the colour brick and move your counter to the next square of the colour you have thrown. Follow the arrows round. The first one to reach the chequered flag is the winner.

Choose your colour
which will it be?
Red or yellow . . .
it's blue for me.
Who will come first?
Wait and see!

Make a spinner

Trace this hexagon shape onto thick card and colour each section to match the cars and mice above. Push a sharp pencil or stick through the middle. Or cover each side of a wooden brick with different coloured paper and throw it as you would a dice.

Shapes All Around

Can you see the shapes in Milly Mouse's car?

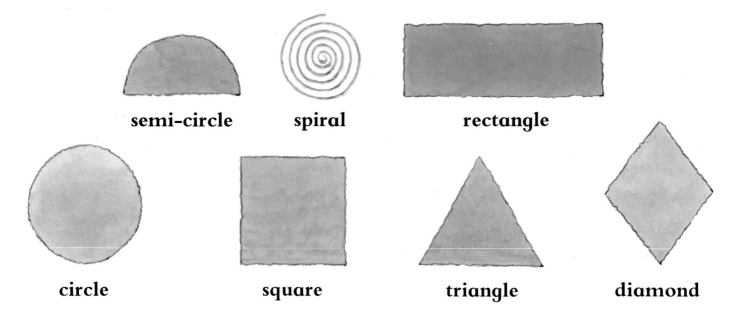

semi-circle   **spiral**   **rectangle**

circle   **square**   **triangle**   **diamond**

How many circles? How many squares?

star

oval

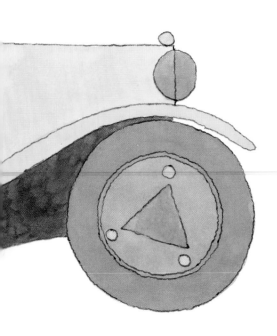

Hanging shapes

Cut coloured card into different shapes and make slits in them as shown.

Join the shapes together at right angles and fasten with sticky tape.

Hang them from string as decorations or mobiles.

Make larger mobiles from shapes cut from different kinds of paper and hung from a coathanger. Shiny paper will reflect the light. Experiment with spirals and cut-outs too.

The Story of the Frog Prince

Once upon a time there lived a princess whose favourite toy was a golden ball. Every day she would go into the gardens of her father's palace and play with her golden ball. And every day as she played two big frog eyes would rise up out of the water of the palace well and watch her. But the princess did not know this.

Then one day as the princess stretched out her hands to catch the ball it slipped through her fingers. Across the grass it bounced and PLOP! into the waters of the deep, deep well it went.

How the princess cried! Tears ran down her cheeks until, through her sobs, she heard a small voice say, "Don't cry, Princess. If I get you back your ball what will you give me in return?"

And there, looking at her with his big sad eyes, was a very large frog.

"Oh anything, anything!" cried the Princess. "Would you like jewels or gold?"

"All I want," said the frog, "is to be your companion. I should like to play with you, to eat with you at your table and at night to sleep in your bed."

"Oh I promise, I promise," cried the princess and, straight away, the frog dived into the waters of the deep, deep well and, moments later, returned with the golden ball.

But the princess – who secretly thought frogs were nasty, slimy creatures – snatched the ball and ran back as fast as she could to the Palace, leaving the poor frog all on his own.

That night, as she sat eating her supper, there was the sound of a splish, splash, splosh outside the door and a small voice said:

"Great King's daughter, open to me
Remember the promise you gave to me."

"What promise is that?" asked the King, and the princess, very ashamed of herself, told him the story of the lost ball.

"Then you must keep your promise," he said. "The frog must be your companion and eat at table with you and sleep in your bed at night."

Well, there was no escape. Much as she disliked the wet, green creature the princess had to share her supper with the frog and when she went off to bed the frog hopped along after her, very pleased with himself.

But as soon as the princess was alone with him in her bedroom, where no one could see them, she picked up the frog and threw him across the room. "Do you think I'd let a thing like you sleep in my bed?" she cried.

The frog lay motionless on the floor, only his great sad eyes watching her. And suddenly the princess was full of sorrow. "Oh frog," she cried, "I'm so sorry – I didn't mean to hurt you." And she picked up the little creature, stroked him and kissed his poor wet face.

And what happened? Hey presto: the frog disappeared and in his place stood a handsome prince. "A wicked witch turned me into the shape of a frog," he said. "Only the love of a Princess could free me from the spell."

Well of course the princess was astonished – and extremely pleased – and it wasn't long before she agreed to marry him and travel with him to his own land and live with him in his palace.

So the Frog Prince's wish came true after all. He was able to be the princess's dear companion and live with her all his life.

In the Kitchen

Biscuits

100 grams plain flour
100 grams sugar
50 grams butter or margarine
1 tsp baking powder
1 beaten egg

Cream the butter and the sugar together. Gradually add the beaten egg. Mix in the flour and baking powder and stir into a stiff paste. Add flavouring like chocolate pieces or grated cheese (but omit the sugar if you make savoury biscuits). Roll out onto a floured surface and cut out the biscuits with cutters. Place on a baking tray and bake at 170°C (275°F/Mark 5) for about 10 minutes.

Pat-a-cake, pat-a-cake, Baker's man,
Bake me a cake as fast as you can.
Pat it and prick it and mark it with B
And put it in the oven for baby and me.

Biscuit faces

Pipe cream or chocolate faces onto plain round biscuits. Use sweets or fruit to decorate.

Models

Make models from dough.
See recipes on page 92.

★ *More accidents occur in the kitchen than in any other part of the house. Never leave your child unsupervised.*

Here are some other foods children can help to make:

Milk shakes

Stir or blend mashed soft fruit into milk. A scoop of ice cream makes it creamier.

Flavoured yoghurt

Mix chopped fruit, nuts, honey or raisins into plain yoghurt.

Sandwiches

Add slices of tomato or cucumber and strips of pepper to make your favourite sandwiches into butterflies or fish.

Or use a pastry or biscuit cutter to make sandwiches into interesting shapes. Roll a sandwich up then cut across it into slices to make pinwheels.

Kitchen experiments

Cut apples into halves then quarters. Which weighs most? Which weighs least? Fill several glass jars with water and add something different like soap powder, sugar, sand, cooking oil, ice cubes or paint to each one. Talk about what happens. Does it dissolve? Does it float? Try with hot water too.

Put an egg into a jar of cold water. It will sink. Take the egg out and stir two spoonfuls of salt into the water. The egg will now float because the solution is denser.

Growing Things

Seeds

Try sprinkling a handful of fast-growing seeds like cress, grass or wheat onto damp blotting paper or cotton wool kept moist in a dish. Put it in a warm dark place and the seedlings should appear in a few days. Try sowing cress seeds in the shape of your name or initials. Then you can eat the results!

Vegetables

Make a desert island by placing the sliced top of a carrot or parsnip in a saucer of water. Leaves will sprout in a few days.

Oats and beans and barley grow,
Oats and beans and barley grow,
But not you nor I nor anyone know,
How oats and beans and barley grow.

Beans and peas

Line a glass jar with damp tissue or blotting paper. Put a few dried beans or peas between the glass and the paper. Fill the jar with water and keep it in a warm place. Watch the roots grow first and then the shoots. When they are larger, plant them in pots or the ground.

Plant experiments

Put a stick of celery into a jar of coloured water. In a few hours, you will see the colour moving up the stem as the celery 'drinks' the water.

I planted a seed,
but nothing grew.
I waited and watched
and watered it too.
Just as I thought it
would never appear,
It popped up a shoot
to say "I'm here!"

Try sticking a piece of black paper (perhaps in the shape of your child's initials) onto a leaf growing outside in spring. When you take it off after a few weeks the initials will be a paler colour where no light has been able to reach.

Bulbs

In the autumn buy some bulbs and bulb fibre. Put some damp fibre in a bowl, place the bulbs on top and cover with the rest of the fibre, keeping the bulbs near the surface. Put the bowl in a dark, warm place for about 2 weeks. When the shoots appear, move the bowl into the light.

Sand

Sand trickles through fingers and oozes around toes. It can be built up and knocked down, made into shapes or used to bury things. You can buy a sandpit or make one from a large box with a solid base (make sure it is covered when not in use). Avoid anything sharp-edged as sandpit toys. They can be buried and become dangerous.

Use saucepans or colanders as moulds for cakes and pies and shells and stones as decorations.

Plastic buckets make the best castles and paper, sticks or twigs make flags.

When I was down beside the sea,
A wooden spade they gave to me,
To dig the sandy shore.
R. L. Stevenson

and Water

Outdoors in the summer or indoors at bathtime, sponges, funnels, sieves and colanders all make good water toys. Don't leave children unattended in or near water. There is a bubble recipe on page 92.

Make a waterfall

Makes holes in yoghurt pots then string them together. Pour water into the top one and let it trickle down.

Make a dam system

Fill hollows of sand with water and use pipes to connect them.

Counting Cats

1

Father Cat is far too fat
To fit on this mat.

2

I think he needs two
Fetch another one, do.

3

It seems to me
That he'll need three.

4

He still needs more
That makes four!

5

How *can* he contrive
To stretch across five?

6

Now what a fix
If we can't find six.

One To Ten

7

"This would be heaven
If I just had seven!"

8

"Please don't be late
With number eight."

9

"I mustn't whine
But I could do with nine."

10

Did you ever know when
A cat stretched to *ten*?

Although he's fat
This cat can have
Only *one* mat!

One Fire Engine

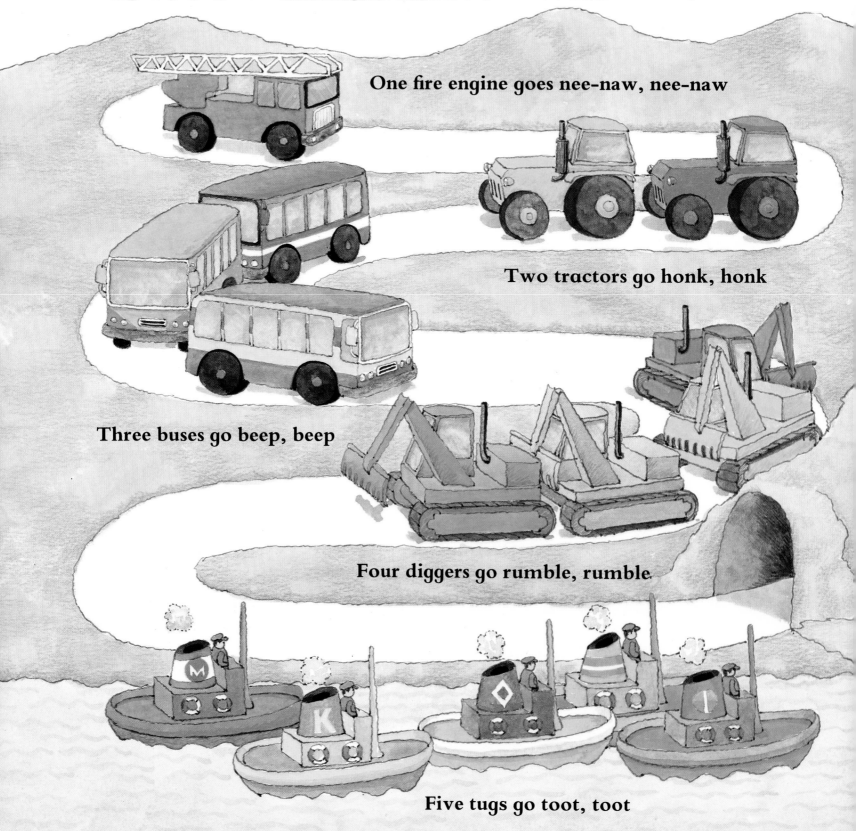

One fire engine goes nee-naw, nee-naw

Two tractors go honk, honk

Three buses go beep, beep

Four diggers go rumble, rumble

Five tugs go toot, toot

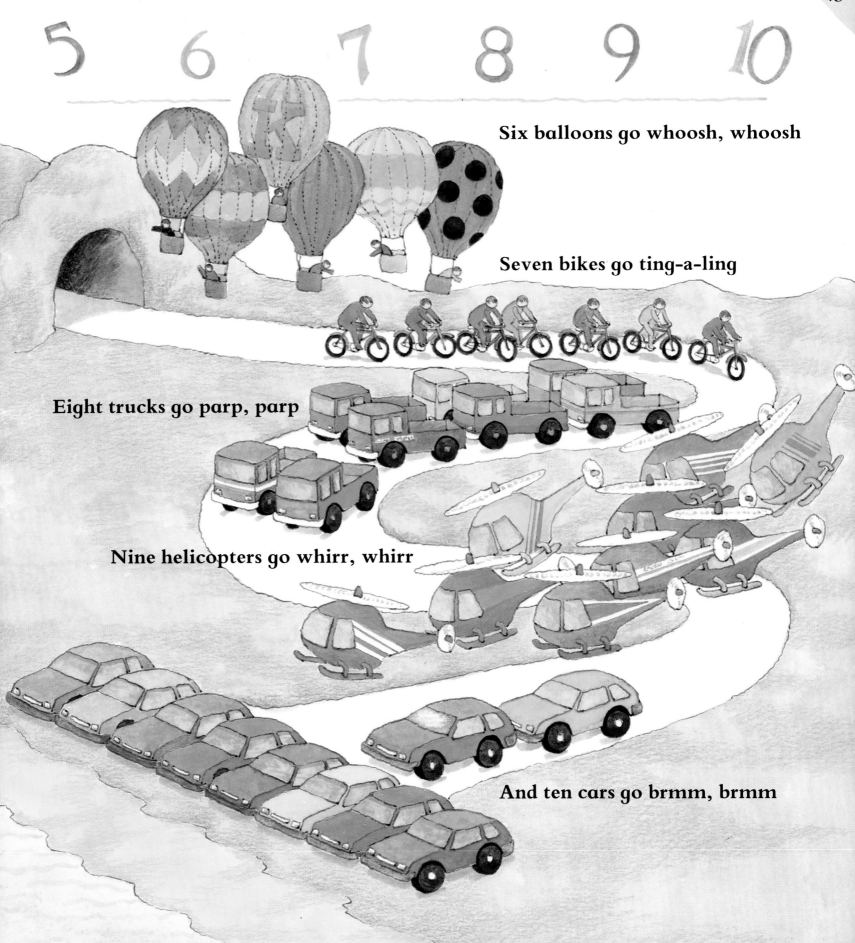

5 6 7 8 9 10

Six balloons go whoosh, whoosh

Seven bikes go ting-a-ling

Eight trucks go parp, parp

Nine helicopters go whirr, whirr

And ten cars go brmm, brmm

A Cherry Stone Game

How to play

You'll need a counter for each player and a dice. Take turns to throw the dice and move the number shown. Whoever reaches the kitchen door first is the winner.

One, two, three, four
Mary at the kitchen door.
Five, six, seven, eight
Eating cherries off a plate.

Soldier

Sailor

Richman

Queen

Poorman

Thief

Beggarman

Where Do Animals Live?

In the snow, polar bear

In the fields, hare

In the forest, moose

In the sky, dragonfly

In the woods, racoon

In the jungle, tiger

In the river, hippopotamus

In the desert, camel

In the pond, frog

On the plains, zebra

In a cave, bat

And what's this I see
A head and a tail
In the deep blue ocean
An enormous WHALE!

Who Lives Here?

a palace for a princess

a den for a robber

a spacehouse for an astronaut

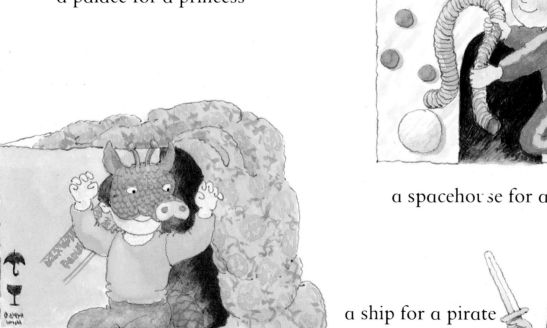

a cave for a monster

a ship for a pirate

. . . and a house for a mouse!

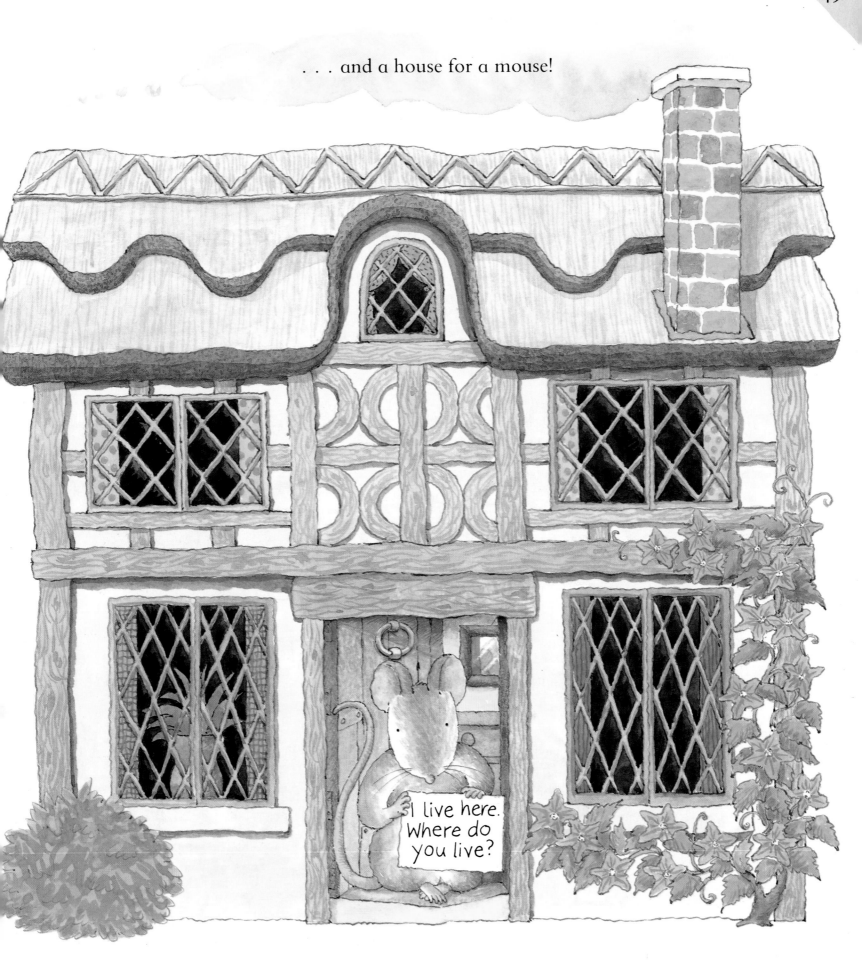

The Story of the House

Once upon a time a pig with a curly tail grew tired of living in his sty.

"I think," he said to his friend, the sheep, "I shall build myself a house."

"Good idea," said Sheep.

"On a hill," said Pig.

"Oooh," said Sheep, "can I come too?"

"Well," said Pig, "what can you do to help?"

Sheep thought and then, "I can pull the logs to build the walls," he said.

"Come on then," said Pig.

So the two of them, Pig and Sheep, went off together and on the road they met a goose.

"Good morning, Pig," said Goose. "Good morning, Sheep. Where are you two going?"

"We're going to build a house," said Pig.

"On a hill," said Sheep.

"Oooh," said Goose, "can I come too?"

"Well," said Pig, "what can you do to help?"

Goose thought and then "I can collect moss with my sharp beak," she said, "and I can stuff it into the cracks of the logs. That will keep out the wind and the rain."

"Come on then," said Pig.

on the Hill

So the three of them, Pig, Sheep and Goose, went off together and on the way they met a rabbit.

"Good morning, Pig," said Rabbit. "And good morning, Sheep and Goose. Where are you three going?"

"We're going to build a house," said Pig.

"On a hill," said Sheep.

"With logs and moss," said Goose.

"Oooh," said Rabbit. "Can I come too?"

"Well," said Pig, "what can you do to help?"

Rabbit thought and then, "I could dig the holes for the logs," he said.

"Come on, then," said Pig.

So the four of them, Pig, Sheep, Goose and Rabbit, went off together and on the way they met a cockerel.

"Good morning Pig, Sheep, Goose and Rabbit," he said. "Where are you four going?"

"We're going to build a house," said Pig.

"On a hill," said Sheep.

"With logs for walls," said Goose, "and moss to keep the wind out."

"And holes to keep the logs in place," said Rabbit.

"Oooh," said Cock, "can I come too?"

"Well, said Pig, "what can you do to help?"

Cock thought and then, "I can crow very early each morning," he said, "and wake you up to begin your work."

"Come on, then," said Pig.

So the five of them, Pig, Sheep, Goose, Rabbit and Cock, went off together. And soon they came to a hill.

"There," said Pig, "is where I shall build my house."

And they all set to work.

Pig sniffed out the logs with his big snout; Sheep pulled them up the hill with his strong legs; Goose dug up moss with his sharp beak and stuffed it into the cracks. And Rabbit dug holes for the posts.

And every morning, very early, Cock crowed to wake them all up so they could begin their work.

The house grew and grew. The walls went up. The windows went in. The roof went on. They all sat back and looked at the house they had built on the hill.

Then Cock flew up on to the roof and crowed and crowed with delight.

> "Cock a doodle doo!
> Just come and look please do!
> We've worked away with such a will,
> To build this house upon the hill.
> Don't you think we've built it well?
> And now inside we mean to dwell!"

Then everyone who lived for miles around heard the Cock's song and knew that the house on the hill was finished.

And when they looked towards the house they saw lights in the windows and smoke rising from the chimney and they knew that inside the house the five friends were sitting together in great happiness.

Building . . . Outside

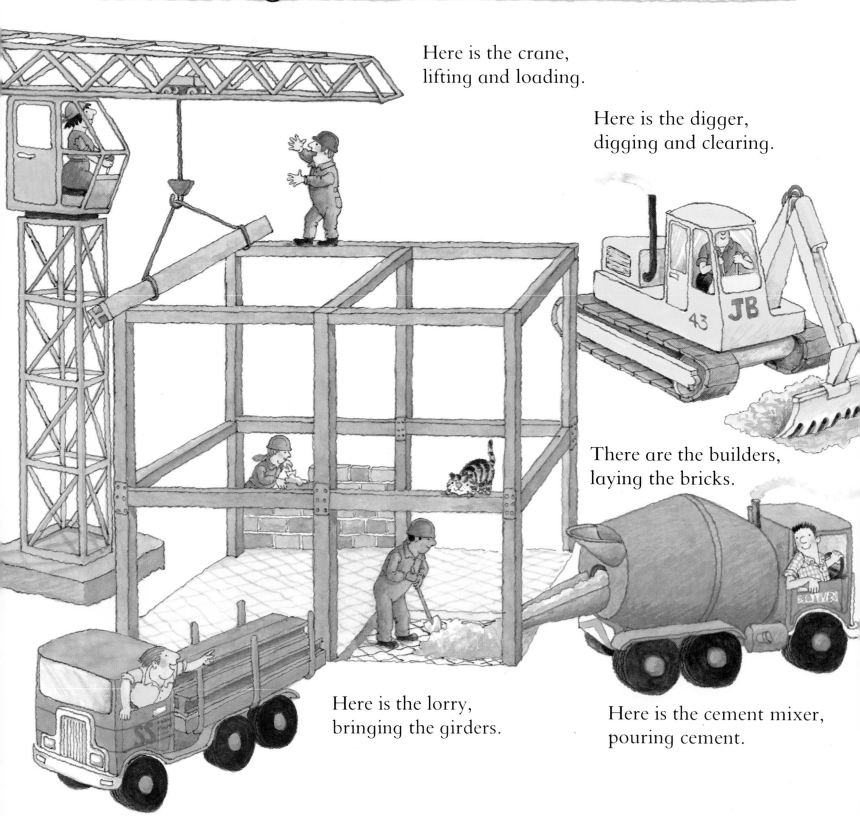

Here is the crane,
lifting and loading.

Here is the digger,
digging and clearing.

There are the builders,
laying the bricks.

Here is the lorry,
bringing the girders.

Here is the cement mixer,
pouring cement.

. . . and Inside

Here are the plumbers, fixing in pipes
Here are the electricians, to put in the lights.
Here are the windows and there are the doors.
Here are the carpenters, making the floors.

And here are the people who're living inside.

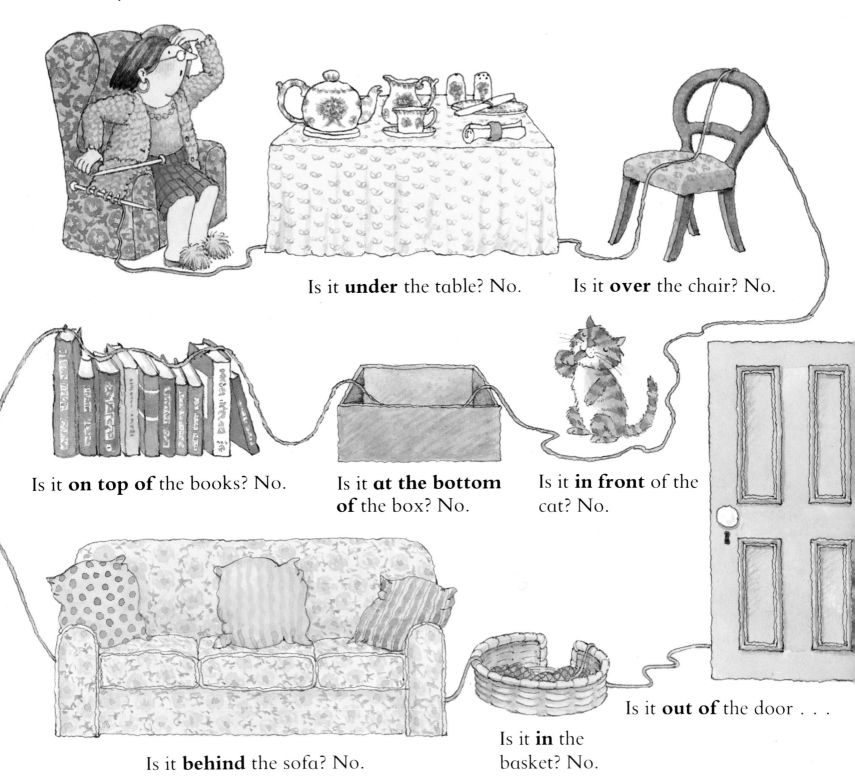

Where's the wool?

Granny wants to knit, but she can't find her ball of wool.

Is it **under** the table? No.

Is it **over** the chair? No.

Is it **on top of** the books? No.

Is it **at the bottom of** the box? No.

Is it **in front** of the cat? No.

Is it **behind** the sofa? No.

Is it **in** the basket? No.

Is it **out of** the door . . .

Here It Is!

Plaiting

Plait by using different coloured strands of thick wool. Tie to the arm of a chair at the start.

Two thick plaits can make a doll. Tie wool tightly around as shown to make the head, waist and legs and sew on arms and features. (See the notes on stitches on page 90). Plaits can also be stitched into mats or stuck onto card to make pictures.

God's eye weaving

Take two sticks and tie them tightly together with one end of a ball of wool. Hold the sticks in one hand and wind the wool around them clockwise and round and round each stick on the way. Change the colour when you like. These make good Christmas decorations.

Woolly Things

Pompoms

Cut two circles of card and make holes in the centre of each. Wind wool around the rings until they are full. Tie a piece of thread between the cards, cut the wool, pull out the cards, then fluff out the pompom.

Slotted card weaving

Cut slots from a circle of card then weave wool around them. Pull up the sides up as you go to make a bowl.

Threading

Practise threading and tying shoelaces. Draw a large boot or shoe onto a piece of card. Make holes for the eyelets and use a piece of wool as the laces.

Baa, baa, black sheep,
Have you any wool?
Yes, sir, yes, sir,
Three bags full;
One for the master,
And one for the dame,
And one for the little boy
Who lives down the lane.

A sheep's haircut

Wool comes from a sheep's coat. It is called a fleece. In spring, the fleece is cut off so that the sheep don't get too hot. It is cleaned, dyed, twisted into yarn and then wound into balls of wool.

Puppets

Do-it-yourself puppets are easy to make using scraps of material, wool, string, buttons and beads. (There are notes on knots and stitches on page 90.)

Wooden spoon puppet

Paint on a face, add hair and tie or glue on material as clothing.

Finger puppets

The simplest puppets are faces drawn onto fingers with a felt-tip pen. The cut-off fingers of an old glove, little bags of felt and even egg shells also make good finger puppets.

Matchbox puppet

Draw a face on the inside of an empty matchbox. Cut two holes in the outer box and one in the back and use your fingers as legs.

Scissor puppet

Cut out a cardboard figure about 12cm high. Make two holes for your fingers as the legs.

Dance, Thumbkin, dance;
Dance, ye merry men, every one;
But Thumbkin, he can dance alone.
Dance, Thumbkin, dance.

Paperbag puppet

Draw a face onto a paper bag. Twist the corners to make ears.

Sock puppet

Paint a face or sew features onto an old sock. Stitch either side of the place where your fingers will make the mouth to hold the shape.

Tube puppet

Paint a face onto a cardboard tube. Glue some material around the bottom to hide your hand and paint or glue on features and hair.

Witch puppet

Tie a handkerchief around your wrist. Paint eyes between your first and second fingers.

I'm king of the land of make-believe,
My subjects do as I say.
There is no end to the fun we have
Or the stories and games we play.

Make a stage

You can use the top of a table as a simple stage or make a more elaborate theatre from a large cardboard box. Fix material as curtains looped to each side. Paint a scene on the back of the box. Change the sets by painting other scenes onto squares of cardboard fixed to sticks and hung over the sides of the box. Glue puppets onto sticks and lower them onto the stage.

Masks

All these masks can be made from cardboard. Cut the pieces to the sizes shown and glue or staple them together. Hold the mask up to decide where the eye holes should be and cut them out. Paint on a face or use wool, felt or pipe cleaners to make features. Cut out ears to the appropriate shape and glue them on. Make two small holes at either side of the mask and knot a piece of elastic through them to keep the mask on.

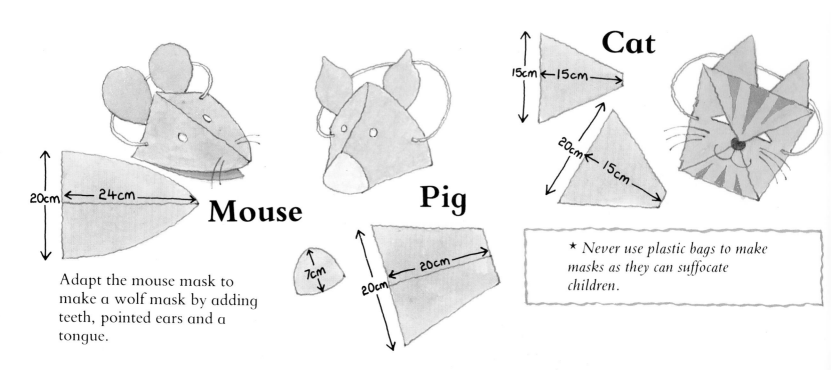

Mouse

20cm ← 24cm →

Adapt the mouse mask to make a wolf mask by adding teeth, pointed ears and a tongue.

Pig

7cm

20cm — 20cm →

Cat

15cm ← 15cm →

20cm ← 15cm →

* Never use plastic bags to make masks as they can suffocate children.

and Hats

Make these hats from scrap paper or cardboard. Paint on decorations or use foil, wool, glitter, even milk bottle tops.

Pirate's hat

Cut a piece of paper about 18cm square. Fold it in half then fold two equal triangles down from the folded edge. Turn up the strip of paper at the bottom, then turn the hat over and do the same on the other side. Paint on a skull and crossbones.

Witch's hat

Cut out a ring of card to fit your child's head. Make a cone and cut a fringe around the bottom. Fix the ring over the fringe and decorate the hat with shiny paper.

Crown

Put a strip of card around your child's head and cut it to the right length. Cut triangles out of the top and decorate with shiny paper, foil or glitter.

Clown's hat

Make several brightly coloured pompoms (see page 59). Glue them on to a cardboard cone or an old bobble hat. Stick some coloured hair around the inside to make a clown's wig.

People

Builder **Farmer** **Teacher** **Cobbler**

Paper dolls

Make your own line of people by folding a piece of paper into pleats. Draw a figure on the front, making sure the arms and legs reach the folds. Cut around it, open out and colour in.

London's burning, London's burning,
Fetch the engines, fetch the engines.
Fire! Fire! Fire! Fire!
Pour on water, pour on water.

Elsie Marley has grown so fine,
She won't get up to feed the swine.
She lies in bed till eight or nine,
Lazy Elsie Marley.

Cobbler, cobbler, mend my shoe,
Get it done by half past two.
Stitch it up, and stitch it down,
Then I'll give you half a crown.

Baker　　　　Doctor　　　　Fisherman　　　　Firefighter

Who needs these?

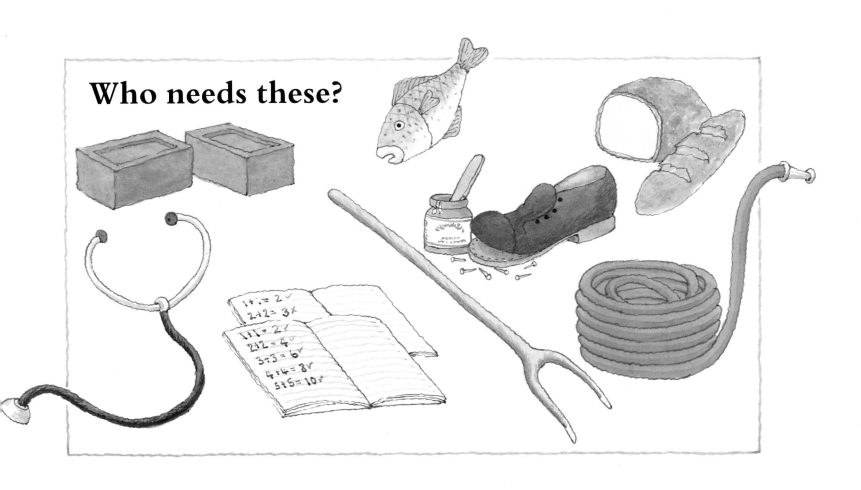

The Story of the Town Mouse

Once upon a time there lived a mouse – a smart sort of fellow – whose home was in a very grand house in a town. Each day he ate the best food, sipped the best wines and at night slept in a warm little hole in the corner of the kitchen floor.

One day, however, he thought he'd like a change. "I could do with a holiday," he thought to himself. "I think I'll go and see my cousin, the country mouse, and get a breath of country air."

So he packed his bag, checked that his hole was clean and tidy to come back to, and off he went.

His cousin was delighted to see him. "Come in, come in," he said. "Make yourself at home while I prepare a special meal for you."

And presently he invited his cousin to come to the table where he had laid a cloth with plates of bread and cheese, a few tomatoes and a small leaf of lettuce.

The town mouse nibbled a little cheese. He took a mouthful or two of tomato and bread; he sipped clear cool water. All the time he was thinking rather longingly of the meal he might be enjoying at his own home – a lamb chop perhaps, a portion of apple pie and cream, perhaps a glass of orange juice. But he quickly put such thoughts aside as being ungrateful because he knew the country mouse was giving him the best food he could find.

"And now," said the country mouse, "you must be tired

and the Country Mouse

after your journey. Let me show you my guest hole.''

And he led him to a small scooped out hole in the bank of a cornfield. Once again, the town mouse thought of his own warm nest, of the delicious smells of food which – all night long – tickled his nose and gave him such pleasant dreams but, once again, he knew his cousin was giving him the best care he could, so he thanked him politely and settled down for the night.

But he could not sleep.

At first, it was too quiet. There were no sounds of traffic outside the door; there were no bursts of conversation from other rooms; there were no footsteps, no distant music such as he could always hear in his own home when the sounds drifted down from upstairs rooms.

He turned and tossed.

Then he began to hear noises. He heard little scrabblings and scratchings as small night creatures came out of their homes and went about their business in the surrounding fields. And then – he shivered with fear at the sound – he heard the great whooping cry of an owl: 'Too-wit! Too-woo!'

And no sooner had he closed his eyes when, ''Breakfast!'' called his cousin. ''Time to get up!'' And there on the breakfast table were a few grains of corn and barley, a glass of water and – nothing else.

How, the town mouse wondered, when he had been so welcomed, could he tell his cousin that he wanted to go home? At last he thought of what to say.

"Dear cousin," he said, "you have made me so welcome that I should like you to come back and stay with me for a few days. It is very quiet here and I think perhaps you would like to see a little of town life?"

"Delighted," said the country mouse and that night they went off together and by dawn were safely inside the town house kitchen.

"Aha!" said the town mouse, rubbing his paws together with delight. "I see there was a party here last night! We have some roast beef, some special ice cream, a few cheeses . . . come and help yourself."

The country mouse gave a squeak of amazement at the sight of such rich food.

But just as they had begun their feast, Crash! Bang! the kitchen door burst open and in came the cook in a great hurry. "Now where's the bacon?" she muttered. "Where are those eggs?" And she rattled and clattered among the shelves of the larder until the country mouse, who was crouched in fear behind a great pitcher of milk, thought he would die of fright.

When the cook had gone, the town mouse – not at all worried – popped out from behind a very large ham, saying cheerfully "All safe now! come on out my dear!"

But every time they began to eat the same thing happened. Crash! Bang! would go the door and in would come someone looking for food, or plates, or a frying pan. There was never a moment's peace.

By night time the country mouse was shaking like a jelly. "Oh it gets worse at night," the town mouse assured him. "That's when we have really big feasts in this house. And the food they leave! You won't believe your eyes."

"I d . . . d . . . don't think I'll be here to see it!" said the country mouse. "I know my food is plain and simple; I know the country life is too quiet for an educated chap like you, but it suits me. And even though the food here is delicious I never get the chance to eat it!" And a great tear rolled sadly down one cheek.

"Oh please," said the town mouse, "don't be upset! I know how it is. Your life suits you but it doesn't suit me. This life suits me but it doesn't suit you – now where's the harm in that? We are both happy where we are and, after all, we can always visit each other from time to time, can't we? It's so much better to live in the way each of us finds most comfortable."

"Ye . . . es," agreed the country mouse. "Can I go now?"

So the town mouse packed a small hamper for his cousin. In it he put a portion of salmon, a slice of pork pie, a little pâté and a few strawberries. "There," he said. "You'll be back home for breakfast! Good bye, cousin, we'll see each other again soon."

And back he went to his kitchen and his rich food, where he never noticed all the interruptions and the noise because he had grown so used to them.

And scurrying along by the hedgerows, crossing fields, the country mouse was making his way back to his quiet little home. Around him he could hear the scrabblings and scratchings of small night creatures looking for food. He heard the great whooping cry of the owl 'Too-wit! Too-woo!' but these were the noises he was used to and they didn't worry him at all.

And at last he came to his own home in the scooped-out bank of the cornfield and, with a sigh of satisfaction, he said to himself, "It's best to stay in the place that suits you best."

So he unpacked his hamper and in the peace of the early morning he ate a hearty breakfast of salmon and strawberries. "The pork pie and pâté I'll save for supper," he said to himself and then, feeling very drowsy after his journey and his large breakfast, he curled himself into a ball and fell fast asleep. With not a sound to disturb him.

A, My Name Is Alice

A, my name is Alice and I sell aeroplanes

B, my name is Billy and I sell boats

C, my name is Cleo and I sell canaries

D, my name is Danny and I sell dragons

E, my name is Emma and I sell elephants

F, my name is Freddy and I sell flowers

G, my name is Gopal and I sell giraffes

H, my name is Hannah and I sell helicopters

I, my name is Izzy and I sell invitations

J, my name is Jake and I sell jeans

K, my name is Katie and I sell kangaroos

L, my name is Lloyd and I sell lions

a b c d e f g h i j k l m n o p q r s t u v w x y z

M, my name is Malik and I sell masks

N, my name is Nancy and I sell nuts

O, my name is Oscar and I sell oranges

P, my name is Polly and I sell parrots

Q, my name is Quentin and I sell
    quarters of cake

R, my name is Richard and I sell ribbons

S, my name is Sarah and I sell snakes

T, my name is Tariq and I sell trains

U, my name is Umberto and I sell uniforms

V, my name is Verity and I sell violins

W, my name is Walter and I sell wigwams

And we three, Xavier, Yim-Mai and Zack,
    do the shopping!

Letters, Words

Writing letters, making cards and sending them to friends and relatives is an enjoyable way to introduce letters and words. There are notes on writing on page 91.

Window card

Cut out a rectangle of paper or card. Fold it in half and cut a square out of the front. Draw a picture on the inside so that it can be seen when the card is closed.

Zigzag card

Fold a strip of paper into a zigzag. Draw on one side and write the message on the pages.

Peek-a-boo card

Cut out a rectangle of paper or card. Fold it in half and open out. Cut off the top left side. Close the card and lightly mark the top of the cut side. Draw a picture on the inside, making sure that only part of it peeps over the top of the line. Rub out the pencil mark.

Word games

Word games can be simple, like 'I spy' or complicated, like this alphabet game.

ALPHABET GAME

The first person says that they are taking a trip to a place beginning with A. The next player repeats the sentence and adds an object they are taking with them beginning with B, and so on through the alphabet.

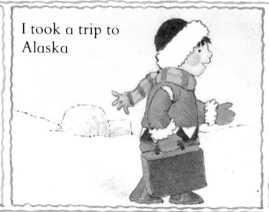

I took a trip to Alaska

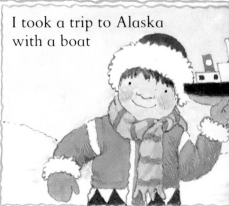

I took a trip to Alaska with a boat

and Scrapbooks

Make your own scrapbooks from thick paper sewn or stapled down the middle. Let your child decide what will go in it – tickets, photos, drawings – and write under each one where it came from or what it reminds you of.

Or make a scrapbook about a specific topic like colour, the alphabet or animals. Draw or cut out pictures of the objects you want and write the name underneath. Encourage your child to draw or find the objects and group them into sets: a page for yellow objects, or objects beginning with A, for example.

Small,

Guess the opposites from the pictures.

If it is not small,
then it is . . .

If it is not quick,
then it is . . .

If it is not tall,
then it is . . .

If it is not wet,
then it is . . .

If it is not hot,
then it is . . .

If it is not fat,
then it is . . .

If it is not new, then it is . . .

Sing a song of sizes
Who will win the prizes?
All our clothes are muddled up
Won't you help us? Do!

Big,

If it is not smooth,
then it is . . .

If it is not noisy,
then it is . . .

If it is not heavy,
then it is . . .

If it is not full,
then it is . . .

If it is not day,
then it is . . .

If it is not dirty,
then it is . . .

If it is not tiny, then it is . . .
(Turn over for a BIG surprise!)

Which is the quickest way to go?
Which is much, much too slow?

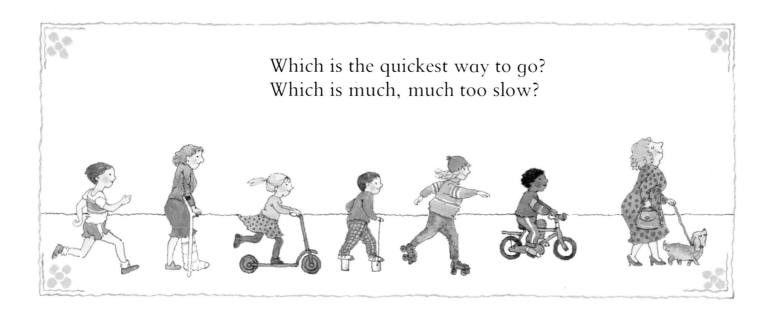

HUGE!

Dinosaurs lived on earth millions
of years ago. Most of them were huge – like this
Stegosaurus (STEG-oh-SAW-rus) which
grew up to 5.6 metres long and could weigh
2 or 3 tonnes. But the biggest dinosaur of
all – Ultrasaurus – could grow
up to 30 metres long and weigh as much
as 30 tonnes. That's about the weight of 25
elephants!

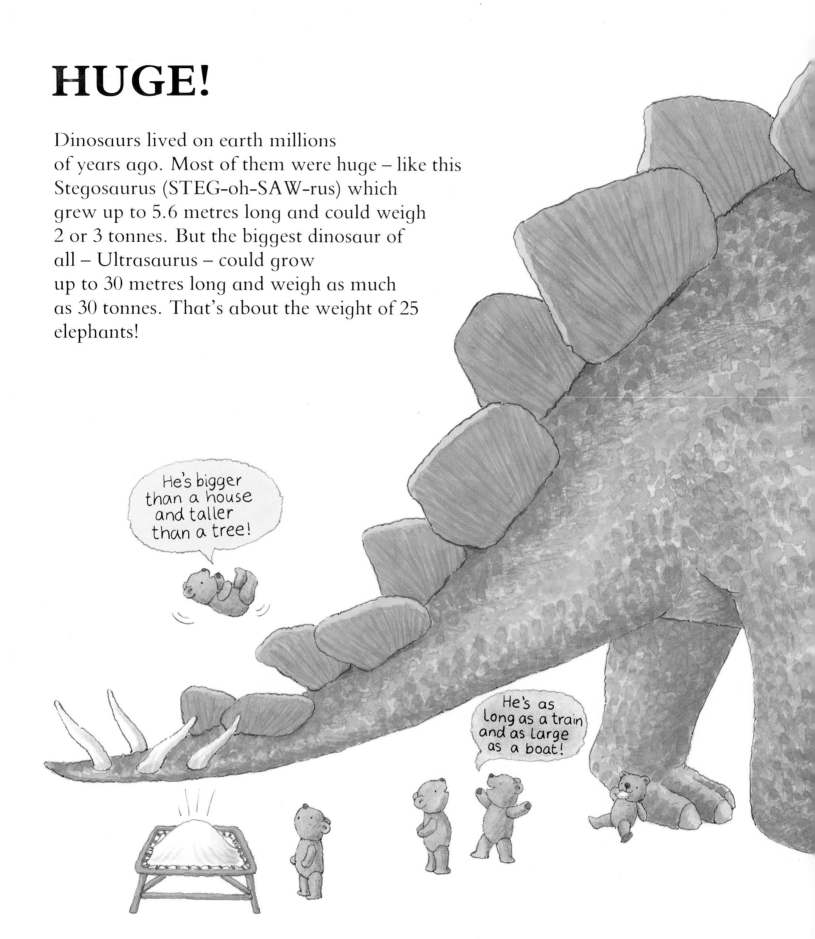

He's bigger
than a house
and taller
than a tree!

He's as
long as a train
and as large
as a boat!

Sneezy, Freezy,

Whether the weather be fine, or whether the weather be not,

Showery
Flowery
Bowery

SPRING

SUMMER

Hoppy
Croppy
Poppy

We'll weather the weather, whatever the weather,

Wheezy
Sneezy
Breezy

AUTUMN

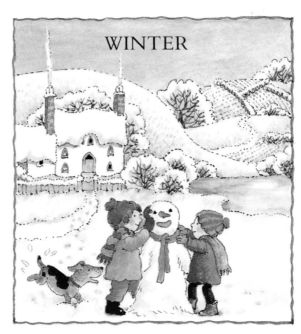

WINTER

Slippy
Drippy
Nippy

Whether we like it or not!

Flowery, Showery

Watch the weather as the seasons change around you. Talk about the different aspects of weather – the clothes you need to wear and what happens to plants and animals, for example.

Shadow stick

Make your own sundial with an upright stick. Mark where the shadow falls at 9, 12, 3 and 6 o'clock.

Who has seen the wind?
Neither I nor you:
But when the leaves hang
  trembling,
The wind is passing through.
Christina Rosetti

I have a little shadow
That goes in and out
  with me
And what can be the
  use of him
Is more than I can see.
R. L. Stevenson

Raindrop race

Each person chooses a drop at the top of a window and the person whose drop reaches the foot of the pane first is the winner.

Bird cake

In winter, mix crumbs, nuts and grated cheese with melted fat in a bowl. Turn out when it is hard and put it in a high place outside.

Rain on the green grass,
Rain on the trees.
Rain on the rooftops,
But not on me.

In the bleak midwinter,
Frosty made wind moan.
Earth stood hard as iron,
Water like a stone.
Christina Rossetti

What's the Time?

What happens first?

Sort out which picture should come first, then second, third and last.

How to make a clock

Cut two hands from cardboard. Fix with a split pin to the centre of a paper plate. Draw on the numbers and a face and add a loop of ribbon or string to hang the clock up.

Make a Hickory Dickory clock

Hickory Dickory Dock,
The mouse ran up
the clock.
The clock struck one,
The mouse ran down,
Hickory Dickory Dock.

Cut a slit above the 6 of the clock. Trace the mouse opposite onto card and colour it. Thread a ribbon through the slit and stick on the mouse. Pull the ribbon to see the mouse run up the clock!

The Story of the Hare

Once upon a time a hare sat looking at a tortoise who was chewing a lettuce leaf.

"You eat slowly," he said, "and you walk slowly. Don't you get tired of always being so slow?"

"Nope," said the tortoise.

"Now I'm very fast," continued the hare. "I can run like the wind. I could run all around this field and back again before you've finished chewing that leaf. Shall I try?"

"Yep," said the tortoise.

Off set the hare . . . *whee . . . whizz . . .* down the field, round the corners . . . *puff, pant, pant, pant* and he screeched to a halt just as the last mouthful was disappearing down the tortoise's throat.

"See what I mean?" he asked.

"Yep," said the tortoise.

"Let's have a race," said the hare. "Of course I'll win but let's see how far I can run. We'll go right round the field and back here. Are you ready?

"Yep," said the tortoise.

Ready, steady, go, and off they went.

The hare raced. The tortoise plodded. *Whee . . . Whizz . . .* the hare looked behind him. The tortoise wasn't even in sight. "Hmm," thought Hare. "I'll just have a snack of those fine looking leaves over there. Plenty of time. Old Plod will never catch me up."

The leaves were delicious. The hare ate and ate. He ate so much his tummy looked like a balloon.

"Whew!" he said. He looked round. The tortoise was *just* in sight . . . plod, plod, plod.

and the Tortoise

So off he raced. Heels in the air, ears flattened. *Whee . . . whizz . . .* screeching round the corner. Then he stopped and looked behind.

No sign of old Plod.

"Oh well," thought Hare. "I'm nearly home again. There's plenty of time for a rest – and I do feel rather full!"

And down he lay in the shade of some bushes and within seconds he was fast asleep.

He slept and he slept. At last he woke. He stretched himself and yawned. "I suppose I'd better finish this race," he thought. "Though there's no need to hurry – I'm nearly home."

So he got to his feet and began to saunter the last few yards. He turned the last corner. And what did he see?

Tortoise chewing a lettuce leaf.

"W . . . wh . . . what's happened?" he stammered. 'H . . . how did you get here? Did you really go all round the field?"

"Yep," said the tortoise.

"You didn't cheat?"

"Nope."

"But . . . but . . . I looked back when I was having a snack . . . you weren't anywhere near."

"Nope."

"And when I woke up from my nap you were nowhere in sight!"

"Nope."

"Then how did you get here first?" asked Hare.

"Just kept plodding," said Plod. "Didn't stop for a snack; didn't stop for a sleep. Just plodded." And he finished the last mouthful of lettuce leaf.

Growing Up

An interest in growing up can be an introduction to a sense of history, especially if you relate it to your own family through stories and old photographs. Make a family tree using stick figure drawings or photos if you have them. Begin as far back as you can and write in the names of all the family members you know.

Arthur Mouse's family tree

Let your child see how he or she is growing as time passes by marking off height on a wall or doorframe once or twice each year. Or make a decorative hanging from a long strip of card or fabric.

Last year's shoes won't fit my feet,
Nor last year's hat my head.
Soon I'll have no clothes to wear
I'll have to stay in bed!
But when I think about it hard,
I think I really know
Like kittens, chicks and even seeds,
All children have to grow!

Stick pieces of paper together to make a long scroll. Divide it into weeks and write down important events which have happened or which you are looking forward to. Draw pictures too.

Times Around the Day

7 o'clock

8 o'clock

9 o'clock

10 o'clock

11 o'clock

12 o'clock

1 o'clock

2 o'clock

3 o'clock

4 o'clock

5 o'clock

6 o'clock

. . . and Night

7 o'clock

8 o'clock

9 o'clock

10 o'clock

11 o'clock

12 o'clock

1 o'clock

2 o'clock

3 o'clock

4 o'clock

5 o'clock

6 o'clock

Time To Sleep

Oh! hush thee, my baby, the night is behind us,
   And black are the waters that sparkled so green.
The moon o'er the combers, looks downward to find us,
   At rest in the hollows that rustle between.
Where billow meets billow, then soft be thy pillow;
   Ah, weary wee flipperling, curl at thy ease.
The storm shall not wake thee,
   Nor shark overtake thee,
Asleep in the arms of the
   Slow-swinging seas.
Rudyard Kipling

What can lambkins do,
All the keen night through?
Nestle by their woolly
   mother,
The careful ewe.

What can nestlings do,
In the nightly dew?
Sleep beneath their
mother's wing,
Till day breaks anew.

If in field or tree,
There might only be,
Such a warm soft sleeping
   place,
Found for me!
Christina Rossetti

Hush–a–bye baby
On the tree top.
When the wind blows,
The cradle will rock;

When the bough breaks,
The cradle will fall;
Down will come baby,
Cradle and all.

Hush–a–bye,
Don't you cry,
Go to sleepy,
Little baby.

When you wake, you
Shall have a cake
And all the pretty
Little horses.

Blacks and bays,
Dapples and greys,
Coach and six
White horses.

Useful Information

Stitches

running stitch   chain stitch   herringbone stitch

blanket stitch

chinese knots

cross stitch

pekinese stitch

Knots

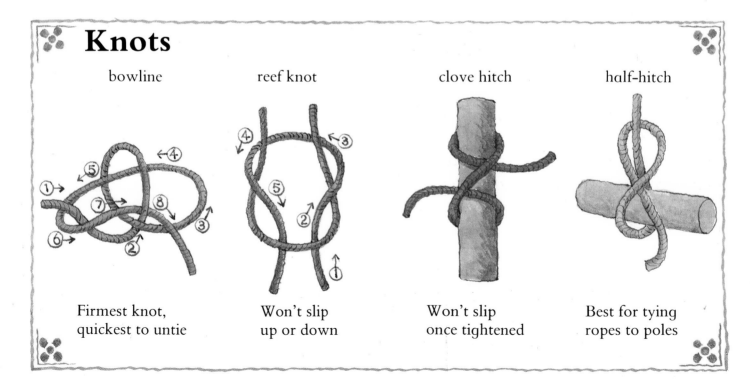

bowline   reef knot   clove hitch   half-hitch

Firmest knot, quickest to untie

Won't slip up or down

Won't slip once tightened

Best for tying ropes to poles

Preparing to read and write

Early reading involves memory, guesswork and lots of help from pictures. Children only learn to recognize words out of context very slowly. They often learn words by recognizing the initial letter and letter sound.

Patterns like these will help your child when he or she begins to form letters. Try drawing them with dotted lines so that your child can trace over them or try to join the dots.

This is how your child should hold a pencil. The index finger should be nearly straight and the hold relaxed. A young child will invariably grip too tightly but will loosen up as confidence and dexterity increase.

Always begin by teaching your child to form lower case letters. The right place to start each letter is shown by the heavy dots. Move the pencil in the direction of the arrows. Don't force your child or make it into a 'lesson'. A child who sees his parents enjoying books will want to learn to read and write.

Useful Information
Recipes

Paste

1 cup flour or cornflour
1 cup cold water
1 cup boiling water
Dissolve the flour in the cold water. Add the boiling water and stir quickly to reduce lumps.

Finger paint

1 cup cornflour or flour
1 cup cold water
3 cups boiling water
Powder paint or food colouring
Make the paste as above then mix in the colouring. Soap powder mixed with very hot water and food colouring also makes good finger paint, as does coloured shaving soap or cold cream.

Bubbles

1 cup washing-up liquid
2 cups water
Mix together well. A ¼ tsp of glycerine or cooking oil added to the mixture will make the bubbles stronger.

Play dough

Mix together 2 cups flour, 1 cup salt, 1 tbsp oil, a little food colouring and 1 cup water. Knead well. The dough will dry out when exposed to air, but will keep for two or three weeks in an airtight container.

Modelling dough you can eat

Cream together 185 grams butter and 250 grams sugar. Add an egg and beat well. Mix in 2½ cups flour. Add flavouring and colouring. This dough needs to be baked at 180°C for 15 minutes if models are 1.5 cm thick or less; thicker shapes will need longer in the oven.

Index